On the Playground

A Ready, Set, Go! Reader

by Liza Charlesworth
illustrated by Louise Forshaw

ISBN 978-0-545-80266-6

12 11 10 9 8 7 6 5   15 16 17 18 19

Printed in the U.S.A.   40
First printing, September 2014

Designed by Maria Mercado

SCHOLASTIC INC.

I run.

I slide.

I swing.

I ride.

I draw.

I kick.

I dig.

I flip.

I throw.

I hop.

I climb.

I stop.

1. What different things did the girl do on the playground?

2. Does she like playing on the playground? How can you tell?

3. What is your favorite thing to do on a playground?